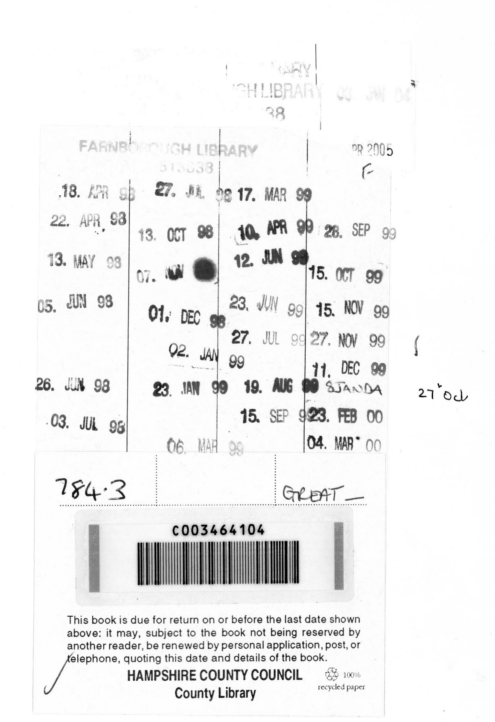

Exclusive Distributors:
Music Sales Limited
8-9 Frith Street,
London W1V 5TZ, England.
Music Sales Pty Limited
120 Rothschild Avenue,
Rosebery, NSW 2018, Australia.

Order No. HLE90000100
ISBN 0-7119-6412-2

Cover design by Pearce Marchbank and Ben May, Studio Twenty, London.

Printed in the USA.

Great Songs of the Fifties

Your Guarantee of Quality
As publishers, we strive to produce every book to the highest commercial standards.
This book has been carefully designed to minimise awkward page turns and
to make playing from it a real pleasure.
Throughout, the printing and binding have been planned to ensure a sturdy,
attractive publication which should give years of enjoyment.
If your copy fails to meet our high standards,
please inform us and we will gladly replace it.

Music Sales' complete catalogue describes thousands of titles
and is available in full colour sections by subject,
direct from Music Sales Limited.
Please state your areas of interest and
send a cheque/postal order for £1.50 for postage to:
Music Sales Limited, Newmarket Road,
Bury St. Edmunds, Suffolk IP33 3YB.

*Visit the Internet Music Shop at
http://www.musicsales.co.uk*

Hal Leonard Europe
Distributed by Music Sales

ALL I HAVE TO DO IS DREAM

By BOUDLEAUX BRYANT

Moderately

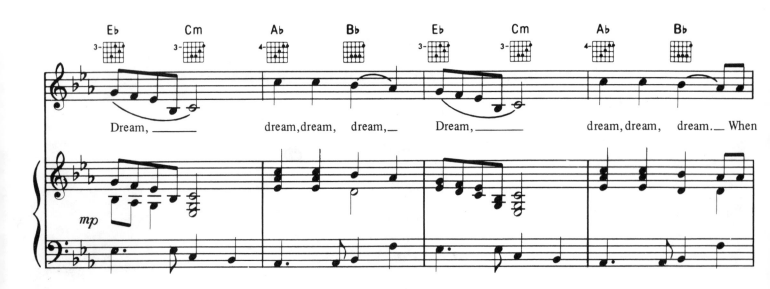

Dream, _____ dream, dream, dream, _____ Dream, _____ dream, dream, dream. _____ When

I want you in my arms, When I want you and all your charms When
I feel blue in the night, And I need you to hold me tight When

ANGEL EYES

Words by EARL BRENT
Music by MATT DENNIS

Moderately Slow

ALL SHOOK UP

Words and Music by OTIS BLACKWELL
and ELVIS PRESLEY

A - well - a, bless my soul,— What's wrong with me?— I'm itch-ing like a man— on a

fuz - zy tree.— My friends say I'm act - in' queer as a bug.— I'm in love. I'm

all shook up!— Mm— mm oh, oh, yeah,— yeah!————————— My

12

Bb

lit - tle mixed up but I'm feel - in' fine___ When I'm near that girl that
in - sides shake like a leaf on a tree, There's on - ly one cure for this

Eb7

F7

I love best, My That's to heart beats so it scares me to death! She
soul of mine, My That's to have beats the so girl that I love __ so __ fine! __ She

Bb

touched my hand, What a chill I got, __ Her kiss - es are like __ a vol -

ca - no that's hot! __ I'm proud to say she's my but - ter - cup, __ I'm in

ALL THE WAY
from THE JOKER IS WILD

Words by SAMMY CAHN
Music by JAMES VAN HEUSEN

When some-bod-y loves you, it's no good un-less he loves you all the
When some-bod-y needs you, it's no good un-less she needs you all the

way.
way.

Hap-py to be near you, when you need some-one to cheer you
Thru the good or lean years and for all the in be-tween years,

all the way.
come what may.

Tall-er_____ than the tall-est tree is,
Who knows_____ where the road will lead us,

ALRIGHT, OKAY, YOU WIN

Words and Music by SID WYCHE
and MAYME WATTS

Moderately, with rhythm

Well, Al - right, _____ O - kay, _____ You Win, _____

I'm in love with you. _ Well, Al - right, _____ O - kay, _____ You Win, _

_____ Ba - by, what can I do? _ I'll _____ do an - y - thing _ you say, _

ARRIVEDERCI ROMA
(Goodbye To Rome)
from the Motion Picture SEVEN HILLS OF ROME

Italian Words by PIETRO GARINE
and SANDRO GIOVANNIN
English Words by CARL SIGMAN
Music by RENATO RASCEL

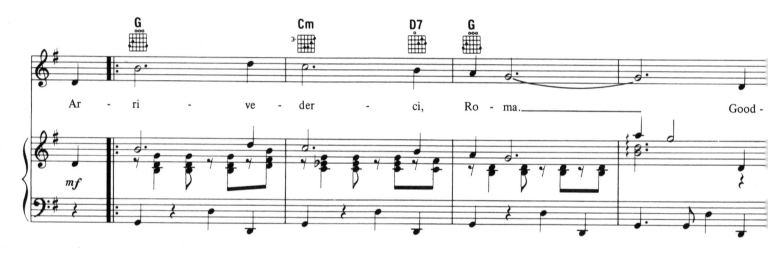

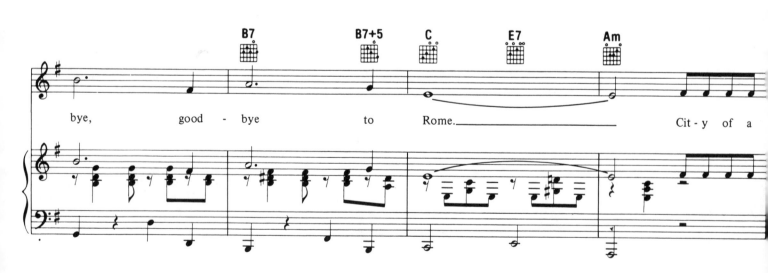

AT THE HOP

Words and Music by ARTHUR SINGER,
JOHN MADARA and DAVID WHITE

Ah ah ah ah, Ah ah ah ah,

Ah ah ah ah, ah ah ah ah, at the

hop.

Well, you can rock it, you can roll it, do the
swing it, you can groove it, you can

BLUE VELVET

Words and Music by BERNIE WAYN
and LEE MORR

BYE BYE LOVE

Words and Music by FELICE BRYAN
and BOUDLEAUX BRYAN

BLUE SUEDE SHOES

Words and Music by
CARL LEE PERKINS

Bright Tempo (not too fast)

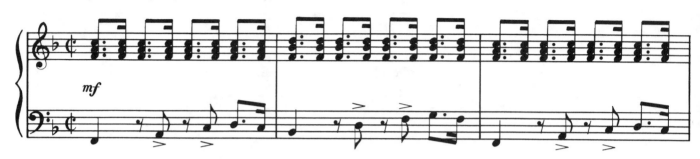

Chorus

Well, it's one for the mon-ey, two for the show,

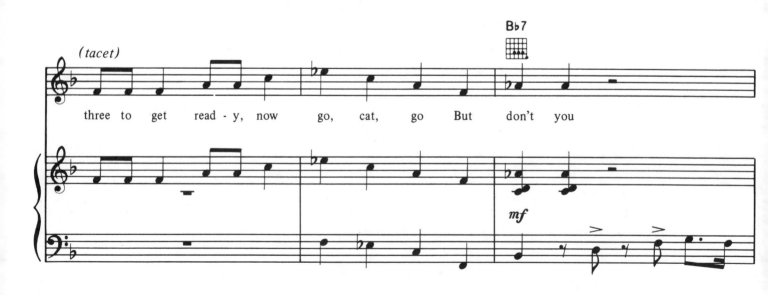

three to get read-y, now go, cat, go But don't you

step on my Blue Suede Shoes. You can

do an-y-thing___ but lay off of my Blue Suede Shoes.___

Well, you can knock me down,___ step on my face,___
Burn my house,___ steal my car,___

slan-der my name all o-ver the place;___ Do an-y-thing that you
drink ___ my ci-der from my old fruit jar;___

C'EST SI BON
(It's So Good)

English Words by JERRY SEELEN
French Words by ANDRE HORNEZ
Music by HENRI BETTI

MCA music publishing

CHANTILLY LACE

Moderate Boogie Woogie

Words and Music by
J.P. RICHARDSON

(Ha - ha - ha - ha - ha)   Spoken: Oh,

you   sweet   thing!   Do   I   what?

Will   I   what?

CLIMB EV'RY MOUNTAIN
from THE SOUND OF MUSIC

Lyrics by OSCAR HAMMERSTEIN II
Music by RICHARD RODGERS

Maestoso

Climb ev - 'ry moun - tain, search high and low,

Fol - low ev - 'ry by - way,

ev - 'ry path you know. Climb ev - 'ry

CRY ME A RIVER

Words and Music by
ARTHUR HAMILTON

DON'T BE CRUEL
(To A Heart That's True)

Words and Music by OTIS BLACKWELL
and ELVIS PRESLEY

Medium Bright (with a beat)

You know I can be found sit-ting home all a-
Ba - by, if I made you mad for some-thing I might have said

lone   If you can't come a - round,   At least, please tel - e -
Please let's for-get the past   The fu - ture looks bright a -

phone.   Don't Be Cruel _____ to a heart that's true.
head.   Don't Be Cruel _____ to a heart that's

FLY ME TO THE MOON
(In Other Words)
Featured in the Motion Picture ONCE AROUND

Words and Music by
BART HOWARD

GETTING TO KNOW YOU
from THE KING AND I

Lyrics by OSCAR HAMMERSTEIN II
Music by RICHARD RODGERS

Refrain (*gracefully and not fast*)

GOOD GOLLY MISS MOLLY

Words and Music by ROBERT BLACKWELL
and JOHN MARSCALCO

Moderate rock tempo

Good gol - ly Miss Mol - ly,

yeah, you sure __ like a ball. __ Well, good gol - ly Miss

Mol - ly, yeah, you sure ___ like a ball. __

HELLO, YOUNG LOVERS
from THE KING AND I

Lyrics by OSCAR HAMMERSTEIN II
Music by RICHARD RODGERS

chance that you'll meet, and you meet not real - ly by

chance. _____ Don't cry, young lov - ers, what -

ev - er you do, don't cry be - cause I'm a

lone. _____ All of my mem - 'ries are

HEARTBREAK HOTEL

Words and Music by MAE BOREN AXTON
TOMMY DURDEN and ELVIS PRESLEY

Blues Tempo

1. Since my ba-by left me found a new place to dwell.
4. If your ba-by leaves you and you have a tale to tell,

Down at the end of Lone-ly Street at Heart-break Ho-tel.
just take a walk down Lone-ly Street to Heart-break Ho-tel.

I get so lone-ly ba-by. I get so lone-ly

I get so lone-ly I could die. 2. Al-

HERE'S THAT RAINY DAY
from CARNIVAL IN FLANDERS

Words by JOHNNY BUR[...]
Music by JIMMY VAN HEUS[...]

(HOW MUCH IS THAT) DOGGIE IN THE WINDOW

Words and Music by
BOB MERRILL

How much is that dog-gie in the win-dow? _____

(Bark, bark!) The one with the wag-gel-y

tail; _____ how much is that dog-gie in the

I BELIEVE

Words and Music by ERVIN DRAKE
IRVIN GRAHAM, JIMMY SHIRL
and AL STILLMAN

Moderately (with much expression)

73

IF I WERE A BELL
from GUYS AND DOLLS

By FRANK LOESSER

Medium Bounce

Ask me how do I feel___ Ask me now that we're co-sy and cling-ing___
how do I feel___ From this Chem-is-try les-son I'm learn-ing___

Well sir, all I can say___ is if I___ were a bell___ I'd be
Well sir, all I can say___ is if I___ were a bridge___ I'd be

ring - ing. _____
burn - ing. _____

From the mo-ment we kissed to-nite___
Yes, I knew my mor-ale would crack___

IN THE WEE SMALL HOURS OF THE MORNING

Words by BOB HILLIA
Music by DAVID MAN

LUCK BE A LADY
from GUYS AND DOLLS

By FRANK LOESSER

let's keep the par - ty po - lite _____

Nev - er get out of my sight _____ Stick with me

ba - by I'm the fel - low you came in with, Luck Be A La - dy,

Luck Be A La - dy, Luck Be A La - dy to - night. _____

8va

INNAMORATA
(Sweetheart)
from the Paramount Picture ARTISTS AND MODELS

Words by JACK BROOKS
Music by HARRY WARREN

JOHNNY B. GOODE

Words and Music by
CHUCK BERRY

Deep down in Lou-'si-an-a, close to New Or-leans,— Way back up in the woods a-mong the
car-ry his gui-tar— in a gun-ny sack,— Go sit be-neath the tree— by the
moth-er told him, "Some-day you will be a man— And you will be the lead-er of a

ev-er-greens;— There stood an old— cab-in made of earth and wood,— Where
rail-road track;— Ol' en-gi-neer in the train— sit-tin' in the shade,— Where
big old band;— Man-y peo-ple com-in' from— miles a-round,— To

lived a coun-try boy— named— John-ny B. Goode.— Who'd nev-er ev-er learned to read or
Strum-min' with the rhy-thm that the driv-ers made.— The peo-ple pass-in' by,— they would
hear you play your mu-sic till the sun goes down.— May-be some day your name-'ll be in

LET IT BE ME
(Je T'appartiens)

English Words by MANN CUR
French Words by PIERRE DELAN(
Music by GILBERT BECAU

MCA music publishing

LOVE ME TENDER

Words and Music by ELVIS PRESLEY
and VERA MATSON

Moderately slow

Verse

1. Love Me Ten - der, love me sweet;
2. Love Me Ten - der, love me long;
3. Love Me Ten - der, love me dear;

Nev - er let me go.   You have made my
Take me to your heart.   For it's made there that
Tell me you are mine.   I'll be yours through

EXTRA VERSE 4. When at last my dreams come true,
Darling, this I know:
Happiness will follow you
Everywhere you go.

MAGIC MOMENTS

Lyric by HAL DAVID
Music by BURT BACHARACH

MISTY

Words by JOHNNY BURKE
Music by ERROLL GARNER

Slowly, with expression

Look at me, I'm as help-less as a kit-ten up a tree And I feel like I'm

cling-ing to a cloud, I can't___ un-der-stand,___ I get mist-y just hold-ing your

hand._____ Walk my way and a

MONA LISA

from the Paramount Picture CAPTAIN CAREY, U.S.A.

Words and Music by JAY LIVINGSTON
and RAY EVANS

Li - sa, Mo - na Li - sa men have named you. You're so

like the la - dy with the mys - tic smile. Is it on - ly 'cause you're lone - ly __ they have

blamed you for that Mo - na Li - sa strange-ness __ in your smile? Do you

smile to tempt a lov - er, __ Mo - na Li - sa, _____ or is

this your way to hide a bro-ken heart? Man-y dreams have been brought to your

door-step. They just lie there, and they die there. Are you

warm, are you real, Mo - na Li - sa, or just a

cold and lone-ly, love-ly work of art? Mo - na art?

MY FAVORITE THINGS
from THE SOUND OF MUSIC

Lyrics by OSCAR HAMMERSTEIN II
Music by RICHARD RODGERS

When the bee stings, When I'm feel - ing sad, _____ I sim - ply re - mem - ber my fa - vor - ite things and then I don't feel so bad. _____

ONLY YOU
(And You Alone)

Words and Music by BUCK RA...
and ANDE RAN...

Slowly, with feeling

Lyrics:

On-ly You can make this world seem right,
You can make this world change in me

On-ly You can make the you are my
for it's true,

dark-ness bright. On-ly You and you a...
des-ti-ny. When you hold my hand, I

To Coda

PEGGY SUE
from THE BUDDY HOLLY STORY

Words and Music by JERRY ALLISON
NORMAN PETTY and BUDDY HOLLY

Oh, well, I love you, gal,___ Yes, I love you, Peg - gy Sue:___

Peg - gy Sue,___

Peg - gy Sue,___ Pret - ty, pret - ty, pret - ty, pret - ty,

Peg - gy Sue,___ Oh, my Peg - gy,_____ My

111

P.S. I LOVE YOU

Words by JOHNNY MERCER
Music by GORDON JENKINS

MCA music publishing

Refrain

Dear, I thought I'd drop a line, The weath-er's cool, the folks are fine;

I'm in bed each night at nine, P. S. I LOVE YOU;

Yes-ter-day we had some rain, But all in all, I can't com-plain;

Was it dust-y on the train? P. S. I LOVE YOU. Write to the Browns just as I do my best to o-

SATIN DOLL
from SOPHISTICATED LADIES

Words by JOHNNY MERCER and BILLY STRAYHORN
Music by DUKE ELLINGTON

Medium Swing

Use pedal sparingly

Dm7   G7   Dm7   G7

Cig - a - rette hold - er   which   wigs me

Em7   A7   Em7   A7   Cm/Eb   D7

o - ver her shoul - er,   she   digs me   Out   cat - tin'

Abm7   Db7-9   C6   F   Em7   A7-9

that   sat - in doll. _____

QUE SERA, SERA
(Whatever Will Be, Will Be)
from THE MAN WHO KNEW TOO MUCH

Words and Music by JAY LIVINGSTON
and RAY EVANS

119

ROCK AROUND THE CLOCK

By MAX C. FREEDMA
and JIMMY DeKNIGH

Swing shuffle

One, two, three o'-clock, four o'-clock rock,

five, six, sev-en o'-clock, eight o'-clock rock, Nine, ten, e-lev-en o'-clock,

twelve o'-clock rock, We're gon-na rock a-round the clock to-night.___

SIXTEEN TONS

Words and Music by
MERLE TRAVIS

Chorus

mind ___ that's ___ weak ___ and a back that's strong. You load
straw - boss ___ said ___ "Well - a bless my soul." You load
high - toned ___ wo -man make me walk the line. You load
night one don't - a get you, then the left one will. You load
Six - teen Tons,

what do you get? ___ An - oth - er day old - er and deep - er in debt. ___ Saint

Pe - ter, don't you call me 'cause I can't go ___ I owe ___ my soul to the

com - pa - ny store. ___
2. I was
3. I was
4. If you

SMILE
Theme from MODERN TIMES

Words by JOHN TURNER and GEOFFREY PARSON

Music by CHARLES CHAPLI

Moderately, with great warmth

Smile, tho' your heart is ach - ing, smile, e - ven tho' it's break - ing.

When there are clouds in the sky, you'll get by, if you smile through your

fear and sor - row, smile and may - be to - mor - row, you'll see the sun come shin - ing

SUMMERTIME IN VENICE
from the Motion Picture SUMMERTIME

English Words by CARL SIGMAN
Music by ICINI

(LET ME BE YOUR) TEDDY BEAR
from LOVING YOU

Words and Music by KAL MANN
and BERNIE LOWE

Medium Bright Rock

Chorus

1. Ba - by, let me be your lov - in' Ted - dy
2. Ba - by, let me be a - round you ev - 'ry

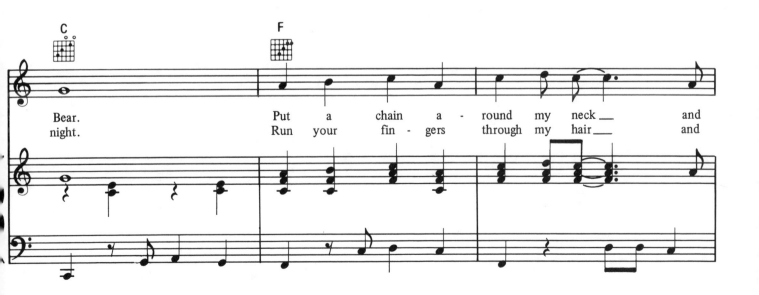

Bear. Put a chain a - round my neck ___ and
night. Run your fin - gers 'round my hair ___ and

130

TENNESSEE WALTZ

Words and Music by REDD STEWART
and PEE WEE KING

THREE COINS IN THE FOUNTAIN
from THREE COINS IN THE FOUNTAIN

Words by SAMMY CAHN
Music by JULE STYNE

THAT'LL BE THE DAY

Words and Music by JERRY ALLISON
NORMAN PETTY and BUDDY HOLLY

TILL THERE WAS YOU
from Meredith Willson's THE MUSIC MAN

By MEREDITH WILLSON

TUTTI FRUTTI

Words and Music by RICHARD PENNIMAN
and D. LA BOSTRIE

145

THE TWELFTH OF NEVER

Words by PAUL FRANCIS WEBSTER
Music by JERRY LIVINGSTON

Very slowly, with feeling

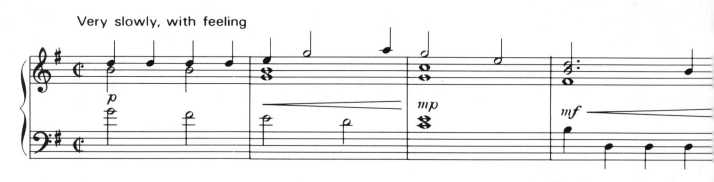

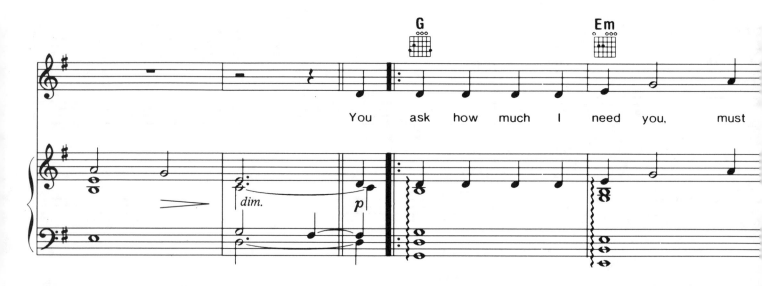

You ask how much I need you, must I ex - plain? I need you, oh, my dar - ling, like

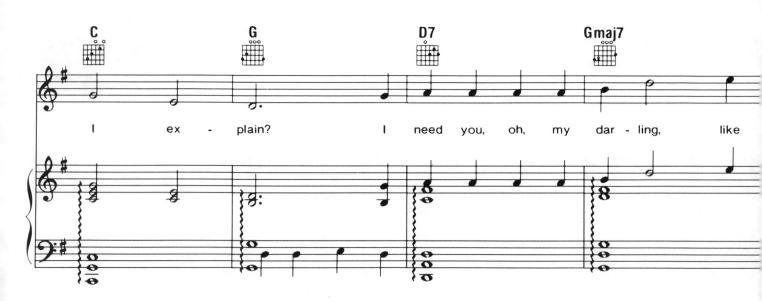

TOO MUCH

Words and Music by LEE ROSENBERG
and BERNIE WEINMAN

Hon - ey, I___ love you too much.
You spend all my mon - ey too much.
Ev - 'ry time I kiss your sweet lips,

Need ___ your ___ lov - in' too much.
Have to share you, hon - ey, too much.
I can feel my heart go flip flip.

Want ___ the ___ thrill of
When I want some lov - in',
I'm ___ such a fool for

WITCHCRAFT

Lyric by CAROLYN LEIGH
Music by CY COLEMAN

154

UNCHAINED MELODY
from the Motion Picture UNCHAINED

Lyric by HY ZARET
Music by ALEX NORTH

WHEN SUNNY GETS BLUE

Lyric by JACK SEGAL
Music by MARVIN FISHER

163

YOUR CHEATIN' HEART

Words and Music by
HANK WILLIAM

USTIC CLASSICS

of the 60s and 70s, including: American Pie
rd • Blowin' In The Wind • Bridge Over
Water • Here Comes The Sun • Leaving On
e • Still Crazy After All These Years •
Starry Starry Night) • Where Have All The
Gone? • Your Song • and more.
0000011

YOU NEED IS LOVE

from the hip years of the late 60s and early
ding: All You Need Is Love • Blowin' In The
orn To Be Wild • Bridge Over Troubled
Hey Joe • Imagine • Light My Fire • Love Her
Magic Carpet Ride • Mr. Tambourine Man •
ration • Riders On The Storm • The Sound
e • The Sunshine Of Your Love • Turn!
rn! • A Whiter Shade Of Pale • and more.
0000044

BOOK OF BROADWAY

, including: All I Ask of You • Another
in Another Hall • Any Dream Will Do •
nd the Beast • Cabaret • Consider Yourself •
ds are a Girl's Best Friend • Edelweiss •
o Know You • I Dreamed a Dream • If I
ich Man • The Impossible Dream • Lambeth
ove Changes Everything • Luck be a Lady
• The Music of the Night • Ol' Man River •
Own • Smoke Gets in Your Eyes • Sun and
Tonight • Unexpected Song • With One
nd more.
0000154

BOOK OF MOVIE SONGS

, including: Airport Love Theme • Baby
Walk • Beauty and the Beast • Blue Velvet •
Feel the Love Tonight • Chim Chim Cher-ee
Romance • Forrest Gump Suite • Heart and
n't it Romantic? • It Could Happen to You •
Time I Saw Paris • Mona Lisa • Moon River
n Soldier • The Rainbow Connection •
ere Out There • Star Trek® • Thanks For The
• Unchained Melody • A Whole New World
ore.
0000165

BIRTH OF
K 'N' ROLL

with historical articles and photos; songs
All Shook Up • Blue Suede Shoes •
y Hill • Earth Angel • Goodnight,
art, Goodnight • Long Tall Sally • Rock
the Clock • Sh-Boom (Life Could Be a
• Tutti Frutti • Whole Lotta Shakin' Goin' On
ore.
0000055

INE

for a better world, including: All You Need
• Circle Of Life • Colors Of The Wind • From
ce • God Help The Outcasts • If I Had A
r • Imagine • The Impossible Dream • The
f The Dream • Someday • Turn! Turn! Turn! •
The World Needs Now Is Love • With A Little
m My Friends • and more.
0000033

LOVE IS BLUE

39 songs, including: Angel Eyes • Crazy • Falling in
Love Again • I Should Care • I'll Never Smile Again •
In a Sentimental Mood • Lush Life • The Man That
Got Away • Smoke Gets In Your Eyes • Solitude • The
Very Thought of You • You Don't Bring Me Flowers •
and more.
HLE90000022

SHAKE, RATTLE, & ROLL

40 songs plus dozens of photos and fun facts about
America of the 1950s; songs include: All I Have to Do
Is Dream • All Shook Up • Book of Love • Bye Bye
Love • Chantilly Lace • Good Golly Miss Molly •
Great Balls of Fire • Have I Told You Lately That I
Love You • Johnny B. Goode • Lollipop • Long Tall
Sally • Maybe Baby • Peggy Sue • Rock Around the
Clock • Shake, Rattle and Roll • Splish Splash •
That'll Be the Day • Unchained Melody • Waterloo •
and more.
HLE90000066

The Decade Series

SONGS OF THE 1920s

46 songs, including: Ain't Misbehavin' • Baby Face •
Can't Help Lovin' Dat Man • Everybody Loves My
Baby • A Garden in the Rain • Honeysuckle Rose • I
Ain't Got Nobody • If I Had You • Louise • Me And
My Shadow • Mean to Me • Miss You • More Than
You Know • My Blue Heaven • Nobody Knows You
When You're Down and Out • Show Me the Way to
Go Home • Sunny • Who? • Why Was I Born? •
You're the Cream in My Coffee • and more.
HLE90000077

SONGS OF THE 1930s

46 songs, including: All the Things You Are • April in
Paris • Blame It on My Youth • Caravan • Cocktails
for Two • A Fine Romance • Heart and Soul • I Can't
Get Started with You • I'm Gonna Sit Right Down
and Write Myself a Letter • In a Sentimental Mood •
Isn't It Romantic? • Lambeth Walk • Moonglow • My
Romance • Pennies from Heaven • Smoke Gets in
Your Eyes • Thanks for the Memory • The Touch of
Your Lips • The Very Thought of You • The Way You
Look Tonight • and more.
HLE90000088

SONGS OF THE 1940s

53 songs, including: All Through the Day •
Anniversary Song • Baby, It's Cold Outside • Besame
Mucho • Blue Champagne • Boogie Woogie Bugle
Boy • Diamonds Are a Girl's Best Friend • Don't Get
Around Much Anymore • Have I Told You Lately That
I Love You • I'll Remember April • I've Got a Lovely
Bunch of Cocoanuts • It Might As Well Be Spring •
It's a Grand Night for Singing • The Last Time I Saw
Paris • Mairzy Doats • The Nearness of You •
Oklahoma • People Will Say We're in Love • Take the
"A" Train • Tangerine • Tuxedo Junction • You'll
Never Walk Alone • and more.
HLE90000099

SONGS OF THE 1950s

55 songs, including: All Shook Up • Angel Eyes •
Arrivederci Roma • Blue Velvet • Chantilly Lace •
Climb Ev'ry Mountain • Cry Me A River • Fly Me To
The Moon • Johnny B. Goode • Let It Be Me • Luck
Be a Lady • Misty • Mona Lisa • Only You (And You
Alone) • Peggy Sue • Que Sera, Sera • Rock Around
the Clock • Satin Doll • That'll Be the Day • Three
Coins in the Fountain • Tutti Fruitti • Unchained
Melody • Witchcraft • and more.
HLE90000100

SONGS OF THE 1960s

52 songs, including: Alfie • Bluesette • Bridge Over
Troubled Water • Can't Help Falling In Love • Crazy
• Crying • Eleanor Rigby • The Girl from Ipanema •
Here, There and Everywhere • If I Had a Hammer •
King of the Road • Leaving on a Jet Plane • Light My
Fire • The Lion Sleeps Tonight • A Man and a
Woman • Moon River • Raindrops Keep Fallin' on
My Head • The Shadow of Your Smile • Something •
Summer Samba (So Nice) • Those Were the Days • A
Time for Us • Twist and Shout • and more.
HLE90000110

SONGS OF THE 1970s

46 songs, including: The Air That I Breathe • Annie's
Song • Band on the Run • The Candy Man • (They
Long to be) Close to You • Copacabana • Crocodile
Rock • Dancing Queen • Don't Cry for Me Argentina
• How Deep Is Your Love • I Don't Know How to
Love Him • Imagine • Killing Me Softly with His
Song • Let It Be • Maybe I'm Amazed • Nights in
White Satin • Rocket Man • Sometimes When We
Touch • You Don't Bring Me Flowers • You Light Up
My Life • and more.
HLE90000121

SONGS OF THE 1980s

39 songs, including: Addicted to Love • Against All
Odds • All I Ask of You • All Out of Love • Axel F •
Candle in the Wind • Don't Worry, Be Happy •
Ebony and Ivory • Every Breath You Take • Hard
Habit to Break • I Dreamed a Dream • Longer • Love
Changes Everything • Memory • Sailing • Somewhere
Out There • Sweet Dreams (Are Made Of This) • Take
My Breath Away • Up Where We Belong • What's
Love Got to Do With It • The Wind Beneath My
Wings • With or Without You • and more.
HLE90000132